DISCOVERING
SIERRA REPTILES
AND AMPHIBIANS

Text and Photographs
by
Harold E. Basey

printed on recycled paper

Table of Contents

ACKNOWLEDGEMENTS iv
FOREWARD v
INTRODUCTION vi
AMPHIBIANS 1
   Tiger Salamander (*Ambystoma tigrinum*) 4
   Long-toed Salamander (*Ambystoma macrodactylum*). 5
   California Newt (*Taricha torosa*). 6
   Ensatina (*Ensatina eschscholtzi*) 7
   Arboreal Salamander (*Aneides lugubris*) 9
   Mount Lyell Salamander (*Hydromantes platycephalus*) 10
   Limestone Salamander (*Hydromantes brunus*) 11
   Relictual Slender Salamander (*Batrachoseps relictus*). 12
   California Slender Salamander (*Batrachoseps attenuatus*) 13
   Western Toad (*Bufo boreas*) 14
   Yosemite Toad (*Bufo canorus*) 15
   Western Spadefoot (*Scaphiopus hammondi*) 16
   Pacific Treefrog (*Hyla regilla*) 17
   Red-Legged Frog (*Rana aurora*). 18
   Foothill Yellow-Legged Frog (*Rana boylei*) 19
   Mountain Yellow-Legged Frog (*Rana mucosa*) 20
   Bullfrog (*Rana catesbeiana*) 21
REPTILES 22
   Western Pond Turtle (*Clemmys marmorata*). 24
   Gilbert's Skink (*Eumeces gilberti*) 25
   Western Fence Lizard (*Sceloporus occidentalis*) 26
   Sagebrush Lizard (*Sceloporus graciosus*). 27
   Western Whiptail (*Cnemidophorus tigris*) 28
   Southern Alligator Lizard (*Gerrhonotus multicarinatus*) 29
   Northern Alligator Lizard (*Gerrhonotus coeruleus*) 30
   California Legless Lizard (*Anniella pulchra*) 31
   Rubber Boa (*Charina bottae*). 32
   Ringneck Snake (*Diadophis punctatus*) 33
   Sharp-Tailed Snake (*Contia tenuis*). 34
   Racer (*Coluber constrictor*) 35
   Striped Racer (*Masticophis lateralis*) 36
   Common Kingsnake (*Lampropeltis getulus*) 37
   California Mountain Kingsnake (*Lampropeltis zonata*) 38
   Common Garter Snake (*Thamnophis sirtalis*) 39
   Western Aquatic Garter Snake (*Thamnophis couchi*) 40
   Western Terrestrial Garter Snake (*Thamnophis elegans*) 41
   Night Snake (*Hypsiglena torquata*). 42
   Gopher Snake (*Pituophis melanoleucus*) 43
   Western Black-Headed Snake (*Tantilla planiceps*) 44
   Western Rattlesnake (*Crotalus viridis*) 45
Index. 49

Acknowledgements

The fun of writing a booklet such as this is the friends one makes along the way. I owe all of the following people a special vote of thanks: J. W. Wright, Stanley W. Elems, Robert C. Stebbins, Arden H. Brame, Jr., Marc Hayes, John M. Brode, Dave Sinclair, Stephen L. Beck, Robert E. Stokes, Steve Arno, Thorne Gray, Henry Berrey, Bill Jones, Jack Gyer, Jane Gyer, Jean Saulsbury, Leonard W. McKenzie, John Palmer, and Dick Burns.

My wife Nola Lee and our three boys, Glenn, Paul, and John, enthusiastically accompanied me on many a herping trip, for which I am appreciative.

Harold E. Basey

The author teaches biology in the Yosemite Junior College District. He has worked more than 20 summers for the National Park Service. Most of these have been as a Supervisory Ranger-Naturalist in Sequoia-Kings Canyon.

Book Design . . . . .Jean Saulsbury
Cover Design . . . . .Kristi Carlson
Range Charts . . . . .Pat Enright

Foreword

by
Jan van Wagtendonk
Yosemite National Park Research Scientist

John Muir once observed that, "When we try to pick out anything by itself, we find it hitched to everything in the universe." His experiences led him to the same conclusion reached by modern ecologists - the natural environment is an intricately woven web of living organisms and non-living substances tied together by dynamic processes. These complex organizations are called ecosystems, where everything is "hitched" to everything else.

Many natural history guides only describe a particular group of organisms and serve as a means of identification. In this book, Harold Basey not only describes Sierra amphibians and reptiles, but also discusses habitat, elevation, and predator-prey relationships. In the broader ecological view, these relationships form the integral ties which give function to the ecosystem.

A food chain is a series of predator-prey relationships and is a classic example of an ecosystem process. Hawks prey on snakes, which in turn eat rodents, salamanders, lizards, frogs, fish and small birds. The chain becomes a web when we consider that birds also prey on lizards, which prey on bird eggs and fledglings in addition to insects and spiders. Such a diversity of relationships is believed to lend stability to an ecosystem, thereby avoiding large fluctuations in population numbers.

The organisms in an ecosystem also have close relationships to the abiotic components of the system. This is exemplified by the dependence of salamanders on moist environments and their physiological and behavioral adaptations to unfavorably dry conditions. The legless lizard has adapted to life underground and depends on insects it finds there. In turn, burrowing activity serves an ecosystem function by mixing and aerating soils. An interesting example of adaptation to the abiotic environment is the protective coloration of the Mt. Lyell Salamander. A better rendition of feldspar-studded granite could not be painted.

A common oversight of many people is the failure to recognize that humans are also tied to the ecosystems in which they live. Although our consumption of frog legs probably has little effect on native populations, other actions often have ramifications which directly affect reptiles and amphibians. The introduction of the Bullfrog poses a threat to the Red-legged Frog. More insidious is the escape from captivity of the clawed frog, a native of Africa. This frog was originally used as the first reliable early pregnancy test. It has many adaptations which allow it to out compete all native species of frogs. Clawed frogs have been reported in California and are extending their range.

Species of limited distribution, such as the Limestone and Mt. Lyell Salamanders, are always vulnerable to human pressure. The well-meaning but uninformed collector could doom these amphibians to extinction. Even the more-common Mountain Yellow-legged Frog has felt the influence of humans. Many of the lakes that this frog inhabited were originally barren of any fish. In our effort to make the parks more attractive to fishermen, trout were planted extensively in their lakes and streams. Since large trout readily eat tadpoles and adults, populations of Yellow-legged Frogs were drastically reduced.

As you read this book and use it for the field identification of amphibians and reptiles, bear in mind the complexities of the environment you are observing. An ecological perspective will give insight into the larger ecosystem we must all share together.

Introduction

The Sierra Nevada is a magnificent 300-mile-long block of granite mountains clothed with many complex natural communities. Thousands of species of plants and animals are a part of this wonderland, their modes of existence intricately intertwined in a mysterious "web of life," which has evolved over many millions of years. The diverse array of creatures which inhabit the Sierra includes two rather obscure, but none-the-less important, groups of animals - the reptiles and amphibians. In this book we will discover more about these little-known, intriguing residents of the Sierra Nevada, who they are, how they live, where they make their homes, and when to find them.

Amphibians and reptiles must absorb warmth from their surroundings in order to maintain body temperatures at levels necessary to carry on their life processes. Such animals are referred to as ectothermic in contrast to endothermic animals, - mammals and birds - which maintain their body temperatures by the production of internal heat from food. Amphibians and reptiles are therefore active only when environmental temperatures are above freezing. So during the colder months, when surface temperatures may drop below freezing, they seek seclusion in non-freezing locations and become dormant.

The geographic area covered by this book is the western slope of the central Sierra Nevada from Lake Tahoe south through Sequoia National Park. This region includes three grand national parks (Yosemite, Kings Canyon and Sequoia) which are administered in the public interest by the National Park Service. Also found in the central Sierra are three national forests (Eldorado, Stanislaus, and Sierra) managed by the U.S. Forest Service.

The Sierra Nevada has been divided into three distinct elevational zones (foothills, Mid-Sierra and High Sierra) to enable the reader to relate to the mountainous topography. The SIERRA FOOTHILLS which occupy lower elevations along the western side of the range, have cool, moist winters and dry, hot summers. A grass-oak woodland is the most common ecosystem type in the lower foothills while at higher reaches, foothill chaparral (bushland) dominates. Streams, with limited riparian vegetation, flow down through the foothills, and rocky outcroppings dot the landscape. The MID-SIERRA, occupying middle elevations, is made up primarily of a mixed-conifer forest composed of varying species of cone bearing trees, including groves of Giant Sequoias. There are also streams, meadows, and rock outcroppings in this area. The HIGH SIERRA occurs at the highest elevations where the climate is colder, with snow coming in fall and persisting in a few places throughout summer. Red fir forests and lodgepole pine forests are found in lower portions of the High Sierra. Higher realms have alpine forests composed of scattered dwarf trees while the highest peaks are above timberline. Many lakes add charm to the High Sierra scene.

All 39 species of amphibians and reptiles known to have established populations in the central Sierra Nevada are discussed in this book. Neither the Leopard Frog, *Rana pipiens,* which has been introduced into the Lake Tahoe basin, nor the Coast Horned Lizard, *Phyrnosoma coronatum,* which occasionally is reported from the central Sierra foothills, are included in the book's text because the status of these two species in the Sierra is not clear to the author.

Reptiles and amphibians are provided full legal protection within the national parks. None should be collected nor harmed within these areas. When outside of national parks, one should consult the latest issue of the state's regulations before collecting any amphibian or reptile, as many are now protected by State and Federal laws.

Amphibians

Amphibians are a distinct class of backboned animals having moist, glandular skins and lacking external scales. The word amphibian comes from Greek and literally means "leading a double life." The name refers to the fact that many adult amphibians live in water or on land with equal ease. The name is also appropriate because most young, or larval, amphibians are aquatic whereas adults are partly or completely terrestrial. Not all Sierran amphibians lead such a dual life, for the lungless salamanders (members of the family Plethodontidae) are fully terrestrial. Their larval "aquatic" life is spent within a terrestrially laid "egg." Upon emergence from the egg coverings they look much like adults and will live their remaining days on land.

There are two distinct groups of amphibians in the Sierra. One includes those with tails - the salamanders. They belong to the order Caudata, which in Latin means "tailed." They have legs of about equal size and superficially resemble lizards. The second group lacks tails when adult. They belong to the order Anura, which in Greek means "tailless", and are called anurans. This group includes the frogs, toads, spadefoots, and treefrogs.

Amphibians, as a group, are distributed from the snow covered peaks of the High Sierra to where the foothills merge with the Great Valley of California. One may find selected species at any time of the year if the right places are carefully scanned. This is not always easy because as the temperature drops below freezing, amphibians may retreat into logs, underground, or to the bottom of ponds and streams, there to become dormant. In early spring, many foothill amphibians may be seen, while at higher elevations, activity may be delayed until late spring or summer. As summer approaches, many foothill amphibians again find underground burrows and take up the dormant life, emerging from summer dormancy with the first soaking rains of fall to remain active until low winter temperatures return. Sometimes favorable humid conditions are present only at night and, therefore, nocturnal activity is very common with foothill amphibians.

All Sierran amphibians (except the lungless salamanders) are found in or near open water during courtship and mating. Anuran voices draw both male and female members of the same species together into an aquatic habitat for egg laying. The voice further serves for sex recognition as usually only males sing. Voices of the different Sierran anurans are easily identified and learning to recognize them in the field adds to the enjoyment of herpetology (the study of amphibians and reptiles). Most male anurans develop enlarged, darkened thumbs during mating season, and in some species the arm muscles also become enlarged. These features facilitate the "love hug," or amplexus, in which the male embraces the female around the chest (waist in the Western Spadefoot) and from behind. They are often hard to separate at this time as external fertilization of the eggs demands that the male be nearby when eggs are laid. Female anurans are usually larger than males and may bulge with eggs ready to be laid. The male's squeezing, during amplexus, may help her expel the eggs. As the eggs are laid, the male is stimulated to release sperm and the eggs are fertilized in the water outside of the female's body. After the eggs are laid, the female quickly loses her robust appearance, the male relaxes his hug and they separate.

Sierran salamanders are silent (except the Arboreal Salamander) and do not have external ears to hear vocal sounds. The opposite sex is recognized by behavior and smell. Some males have odor-producing glands in the skin of the tail and head. He rubs his head and body against a female's head and she may follow him about. After a while, the male deposits a cone of jelly topped by a sperm packet, called a spermatophore. The female picks it up with the lips of her vent and places it inside her body in a receptacle called a spermatheca. After a short time fertilization occurs internally and she later lays fertilized eggs which develop into larval salamanders. Details of courtship and mating are different for each species of amphibian and much is yet to be discovered through close observation.

Amphibian eggs are round, darker on the top than the bottom and are protected by transparent jelly envelopes. They are laid in water or moist sites. Most of the egg's stored food is present in the light colored lower portion. The number and size of eggs will vary among species of amphibians. Anurans, as a rule, lay many eggs, in the thousands, while salamanders usually lay in the hundreds. Toads lay eggs in long strings while frogs' are in masses, up to the size of a bunch of grapes.

The amphibian embryo visibly develops inside the egg's jelly envelopes and wriggles more and more as it grows until it finally breaks free. The entire "egg" cluster is "alive" with wriggling embryos just before hatching. Larval anurans are called tadpoles, or pollywogs, and the Sierran species usually are vegetarians, eating tiny water plants. (The spadefoot tadpole is an exception to this as it eats aquatic insects and sometimes becomes cannibalistic.) The gills of tadpoles are hidden from view beneath a covering of skin while larval salamanders have conspicuous external gills in the neck region, making an obvious difference between young and adult salamanders.

The change in amphibians from aquatic young to terrestrial adult is called metamorphosis and the length of time spent in the larval stage, and then in metamorphosis, varies with the kind of amphibian and the environmental conditions. Cold temperatures retard the development, warmer temperatures speed it. The first obvious sign of transformation in anurans is the appearance of two hind legs at the base of the tail. After the hind legs are well developed and being used to aid the tail in swimming, the front legs appear. The gills are replaced with lungs and the longer intestine (which characterizes a vegetarian) is replaced by a shorter one associated with the predatory diet of the adult. Adult Sierran amphibians are predators, preying on moving animals small enough to capture. They seldom capture animals that are not moving.

Frogs, toads and salamanders make up a merry and varied group of animals and all Sierran ponds and lakes have their own populations of one species or another, as they occur abundantly in most moist locations. They have a complex life cycle, part of which is spent in water and part on land. During the tadpole stage they breathe through gills but when mature and living on land, the gills are replaced by lungs. This sort of adaptive process is repeated many times in nature.

All Sierran frogs and toads prey adroitly and successfully on a great variety of moving insects small enough to be captured and swallowed whole.

John Muir allowed a small portion of Yosemite Creek to flow through a corner of his cabin to provide him with music, especially at night when he lay awake. A few frogs came inside on the stream and added to the musical notes of the water. Muir said of them "What a cheery, hearty set they are, and how bravely their krink and tronk concerts enliven the rocky wilderness!"

Amphibians can be a joy to all but one must have an open mind - and ears - to receive the pleasures they offer.

Tiger Salamander

Ambystoma tigrinum

family
Ambystomidae

Wide distribution is sometimes a measure of a species' success. Against this yardstick, the Tiger Salamander is very successful for it is found in appropriate habitat over much of North America — though it seems unsuccessful in the Sierra, as adults are seldom seen. They are not often encountered because activity takes place primarily during cool, rainy nights - times when few people are in the field. On rare occasions, hundreds are seen during the first soaking fall rains, as they make a nocturnal journey from their grassland burrows to breeding ponds. During the day, they hide beneath protecting surface objects.

Upon reaching the ponds, mating takes place and females later attach eggs to submerged vegetation. The adults often leave the pond shortly after egg-laying has finished. The eggs hatch in a few weeks into gilled larvae that feed primarily on aquatic insects. Larval Tiger Salamanders are sometimes very abundant in these grassland breeding ponds and, if food is abundant, the larvae grow rapidly, leaving the ponds as small adults before summer arrives. They spend the summer in grassland burrows which may have been dug by California Ground Squirrels.

The future of this species in California is uncertain due to pesti-cides draining into breeding ponds, introduced Bullfrogs eating the larvae, the absence of squirrel burrows and grasslands being converted to orchards or vineyards. None occurs within the Sierran national parks.

IDENTIFICATION
Cream to white spots or bars on a background of black. The broad, rounded snout with small protruding eyes characterize larvae as well as adults. Total length to 215 mm (8½ in.).

RANGE
A grassland species of the low foothills and Great Valley. Found all along the Central Sierra, becoming scarcer in the south.

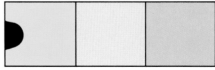

FOOTHILLS	MID-SIERRA	HIGH-SIERRA

Long-Toed Salamander

Ambystoma macrodactylum

family
Ambystomidae

As the Mid-Sierran summer approaches, snow melts and ponds form. At this time, Long-toed Salamanders make their way from under forest objects to ponds where they mate and lay eggs. The adults seldom are encountered away from such breeding sites. When in ponds, they hide during the day under submerged objects, then, in late afternoon and early evening, they venture out and are seen swimming about.

Females lay clusters of 2 - 12 eggs, which they attach to the underside of submerged objects. The eggs, often covered with organic debris providing camouflage, hatch into gilled larvae that may be found in Mid-Sierran ponds during the summer months. Ponds at the lower, warmer elevations provide ample food and here the young often mature to adults during their first summer. At higher elevations the young usually remain in the ponds until the second summer. Once they have become adults, they hide under logs, bark and rocks much of the year.

IDENTIFICATION
A yellowish dorsal stripe with irregular borders; sometimes the *dorsal stripe is broken into yellowish spots*. Total length to 178 mm (7 in.)

RANGE
This species occurs north of the Middle Fork of the Stanislaus River in the Mid-Sierra.

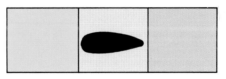

FOOTHILLS   MID-SIERRA   HIGH-SIERRA

Long-Toed Salamander Larva

California Newt

Taricha torosa

family
Salamandridae

The word "newt" is often applied to all salamanders, but correctly refers only to members of the family Salamandridae. Summer finds foothill newts in dormancy under rocks, in deep crevices or in burrows, though a few may be active in lakes and ponds at higher elevations in the lower Mid-Sierra.

With the first soaking rain in autumn, the dormant ones rouse themselves and move toward the surface. During the cooler, wetter winter months they may be found under surface objects or sometimes seen crawling in the open, particularly during rainy times. In late winter and early spring, they make their way to foothill streams, ponds or lakes to mate and lay eggs. Many are seen crossing roads during spring rains, on their way to breeding sites. Experiments indicate that adults may return to the same part of a stream each year, though how they find their way is not understood.

After a rather complex courtship and internal fertilization, a female lays spherical egg masses containing 12 or 16 eggs which are usually attached to submerged vegetation.

When alarmed or injured, California Newts assume a characteristic pose with tail up and over the head, the head bent back over the shoulders. This position exposes the vivid orange undersides which is thought to discourage some predators from attacking, as such bright colors often indicate a toxic animal.

Female California Newt with Eggs

IDENTIFICATION
Dark to light brown on top without spots, unspotted orange to *orange-red underside*. Rough skin when terrestrial and smooth skin when aquatic. Swollen vent of males distinguishes them from females during breeding season. Length to 165 mm (6½ in.).

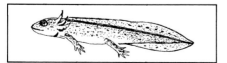

California Newt Larva

RANGE

The length of the Sierra, primarily in the foothills.

FOOTHILLS   MID-SIERRA   HIGH-SIERRA

California Newt in Defensive Pose

Ensatina
Ensatina eschscholtzi

family

Plethodontidae

Walking quietly among towering Giant Sequoias is an inspirational experience; looking occasionally under a log can add to this adventure, for sooner or later this colorful salamander will be found. It is usually discovered in spring and early summer in moist places under fallen limbs, logs and leaves. As its habitat becomes drier in late summer it will go deeper into burrows or into rotting logs.

Being a lungless salamander, like other members of this family, it does not require open water in which to lay eggs. Instead, the female Ensatina lays up to 12 eggs in moist spots such as burrows or decaying logs. The eggs must remain moist and, to help, the

Ensatina in Defensive Pose

female coils her body around them. Her glandular skin produces a fluid that prevents drying, and may also prevent the growth of destructive fungi; she may physically defend her eggs from other animals. When disturbed, a milkish secretion is exuded from an Ensatina's tail. This fluid is thought to be distasteful to predators and to give a degree of protection to Ensatinas.

The Yellow-eyed Salamander (*Ensatina eschscholtzi xanthoptica*), an upper foothill subspecies in the Central Sierra, lacks vivid orange spots. The Sierra Salamander (*Ensatina eschoscholtzi platensis*), a subspecies throughout the Mid-Sierra, has vivid orange spots. The two subspecies coexist from Bass Lake northward into Calaveras County, where the foothills meet the Mid-Sierra.

IDENTIFICATION
A constriction at the base of the tail. Orange blotches are characteristic for most of the Sierra. Plain brownish ones with orange bellies are found in the central foothills. Young have distinctive yellow to orange thighs and lack the adult coloration. Length to 153 mm (6 in.).

RANGE
The length of the Sierra, primarily in the Mid-Sierra, also found in the upper foothills from Calaveras County south into Madera County.

Ensatina, Unspotted Type

FOOTHILLS   MID-SIERRA   HIGH-SIERRA

Arboreal Salamander

Aneides lugubris

family
Plethodontidae

Amphibian sounds are usually associated with frogs and not salamanders. Surprisingly, this salamander may produce squeaking sounds, particularly when first caught. The role of these sounds in the life of this animal is yet to be discovered.

Like other lungless salamanders, it respires through its skin. The skin must remain moist and therefore activity is primarily at night when the humidity is higher. Its diet consists primarily of insects and other small arthropods. Unlike other Sierran salamanders, fungi makes up a portion of its food.

Up to 20 eggs are laid in late spring in moist cavities in the ground, in rotten logs and occasionally in hollows in trees. The eggs hatch in late summer.

Despite the name, it is found in trees only occasionally, although the Interior Live Oak is associated with its distribution. Instead, it is usually found under logs, bark and rocks during the wetter months. It seeks underground burrows, rock crevices and caverns in summer.

IDENTIFICATION

Head is distinctively wedge-shaped with bulging muscles, particularly in adult males. Teeth on the front margin of the upper jaw are prominent. Upper surface dark brown, sometimes with small yellow spots. Total length to 165 mm (6½ in.).

RANGE

Occurs only in the Central Sierra from east of Sacramento south to east of Madera.

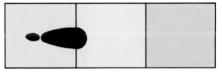

FOOTHILLS   MID-SIERRA   HIGH-SIERRA

Distinctively Wedgeshaped
Head of Arboreal Salamander

Mount Lyell Salamander

Hydromantes platycephalus

family
Plethodontidae

In 1915, a group of scientists from the University of California at Berkeley were camped at the base of Mount Lyell in Yosemite National Park. Trap lines were run through various habitats to ascertain the kinds of mammals inhabiting the area. Unexpectedly, the first recorded specimens of this salamander were caught in a mousetrap and named for the area of discovery. Examination revealed that these newly discovered animals were not related to other recorded salamanders of the Sierra, but instead, resembled salamanders found in Europe.

Since 1915, naturalists visiting the High Sierra have hunted for these scarce animals and have found them in a number of scattered localities. Usually, they are discovered beneath granite rocks lying on a moist surface, some areas are near persistent snow fields. This supports the hypothesis that this salamander is a relic of past glacial days. During those days of extensive glaciers, there was likely one large, unbroken population and the Mount Lyell Salamander occurred in large numbers. Populations are now separated and there are few animals in each. Please don't endanger the species by molesting or collecting them.

The tail of this salamander has a blunt adhesive tip which helps it climb wet granite rocks.

IDENTIFICATION

Head and body flattened, toes partly webbed, short tail. *Coloration flecked like granite rock,* reddish and grayish phases. Tongue mushroom-like and capable of extensive protrusion. Young are greenish. Total length to 140 mm (5½ in.).

RANGE

Scattered populations in the High Sierra from the Sonora Pass area south into Sequoia National Park. Found in all three Sierran national parks.

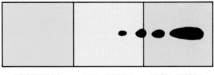

FOOTHILLS   MID-SIERRA   HIGH-SIERRA

Limestone Salamander
Hydromantes brunus

family
Plethodontidae

In 1952, a new species of salamander was discovered in the Merced River Canyon, west of Yosemite National Park. The first word of the scientific name assigned to it, *Hydromantes,* indicates a close relationship to the Mount Lyell Salamander of the High Sierra. The two indeed share many of the same characteristics. For example, each has an unusual mushroom-like tongue, with free margins, that can be extended up to one-third the body length; the tongue is employed to capture moving prey. The common name, Limestone Salamander, is applied to this animal because of its association with the limestone outcroppings of the Merced River Canyon.

The species is still known only from the area of original discovery and appears to be limited to the vicinity of Briceburg and along Bear Creek, a tributary of the Merced River at that location; it has also been reported in the Merced Canyon eight miles below Briceburg. Because of its restricted distribution and few numbers, it is listed as a rare species by the State government. This provides the species and its habitat legal protection. It is therefore unlawful to take or possess this salamander.

IDENTIFICATION
Head and body flattened, toes partly webbed, *uniformly brown above, pale underneath.* Young are greenish yellow, changing with age to yellow, beige and then brown. Total length to 127 mm (5 in.).

RANGE
Restricted to the lower Merced River Canyon.

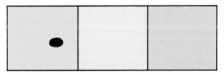

FOOTHILLS   MID-SIERRA   HIGH-SIERRA

11

Relictual Slender Salamander

Batrachoseps relictus

family
Plethodontidae

Slender salamanders, genus *Batrachoseps,* are found only in western Northern America. These are small creatures with elongated bodies, long tails, and tiny limbs. Such features enable them to live successfully in small crevices and burrows. Occupancy of such burrows futher allows them to live in foothill areas where summers may be lethally hot and dry. Unlike most slender salamander species, the Relictual Slender Salamander is found in areas of year-round moisture and it does not become dormant in burrows during the hot season. Its distribution is limited in the upper foothills and Mid-Sierra as there are few suitable areas of permanent moisture.

This little animal appears to be a surviving ancestor of the other Sierran slender salamander species. Relictual means relic and its common name refers to its ancestral role. This species was first described in the scientific literature in 1968; studies of slender salamanders are continuing, with additional discoveries anticipated. There are four similar-looking species of slender salamanders inhabiting the Sierra south of Sequoia National Park; therefore, use caution in identification of slender salamanders in that area.

IDENTIFICATION

Slender and worm-like, short trunk (16 - 20 intercostal grooves), moderately short legs, moderately broad head with protruding eyes. *Grayish, often with white freckles;* with or without a stripe down the back. Total length to 140 mm (5½ in.), usually one-half of this length being tail.

RANGE

In the upper foothills and lower Mid-Sierra from the Merced River southward into the Kern River Canyon. Found in places that do not become totally dry in the summer.

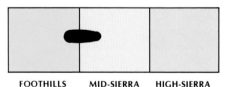

FOOTHILLS   MID-SIERRA   HIGH-SIERRA

California Slender Salamander

Batrachoseps attenuatus

family
Plethodontidae

Unlike most other Sierran amphibians, the slender salamanders will start laying eggs with the first soaking rains of fall. Very little is known about their courtship and mating. The eggs are whitish, about the size of a BB shot and in clusters of up to 12 eggs. Development is slow during the cold winter and the eggs usually hatch in early spring. The young are less than 25 mm (1 in.) long at the time of hatching.

When inactive, Slender Salamanders often coil like serpents, their heads in the center. This is the position in which they may be found when their surface covering is removed. When disturbed they often wriggle rapidly away or they may "play possum." Attempts to capture and hold these wriggling creatures frequently ends with the loss of the salamander's tail. Like lizards, slender salamanders can grow new tails. The broken portion of the tail thrashes about, perhaps diverting a predator.

A white, albino, California Slender Salamander has been found only once in the Sierra.

IDENTIFICATION

Slender and worm-like, long trunk (19 - 21 intercostal grooves), short legs, 10 to 12 costal folds between tips of toes when limbs are held along sides, very narrow head with protruding eyes. Body dark with redddish brown, *tan or yellowish stripe down back.* Total length to 140 mm (5½ in.) with usually over one-half of this length being the tail.

RANGE

In moist foothill woodland situations, such as under limbs, logs, rocks and in leaf litter. They are active from the first fall rains until their habitat becomes dry, at which time they seek burrows for the summer.

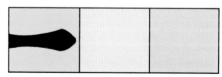

FOOTHILLS   MID-SIERRA   HIGH-SIERRA

Western Toad

Bufo boreas

family
Bufonidae

Western Toads often are active at night, yet they are one of the most familiar amphibians of the Sierran foothills and Great Valley as they thrive in well-watered yards and gardens. An evening stroll through one of these yards usually reveals several toads, often feeding on insects drawn by an outdoor light. If approached, they do not hop or jump; but sit quietly or move away with an awkward, ape-like crawl. Predators could easily catch them. However, a toad's prominent warts produce a milky, seemingly bad-tasting, poisonous fluid that causes most predators to drop them quickly. After its nightly ventures, a toad digs or finds a moist burrow in which to spend the day, returning regularly to the same diurnal hiding place for many days or months and perhaps even years.

When spring rains come, Western Toads move to nearby ponds or streams to breed. The males have a weak, chirping voice which would not seem loud enough to draw females to the breeding site. Instead, adult toads seem to remember (imprinted) the location of their natal homes.

Diurnal activity is common at higher elevations and nocturnal activity is the mode in warmer areas.

Western Toad Tadpole

IDENTIFICATION

Skin has prominent warts and usually *a thin whitish line down the center of the back.* Young have bright yellow or orange undersides to feet. Paratoid glands on side of neck are large and well separated. Body length to 127 mm (5 in.).

RANGE

Usually occurs near streams, ponds, lakes and in meadows the length of the Sierra. Occasionally seen in the High Sierra, but, seldom within the range of the Yosemite Toad.

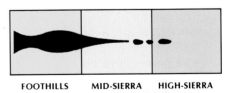

FOOTHILLS   **MID-SIERRA**   **HIGH-SIERRA**

Yosemite Toad
Bufo canorus

family
Bufonidae

Bufo indicates that the Yosemite Toad is a member of the typical toad group. *Canorus* refers to its song, a sustained, melodious trill which, at a distance, sounds like that of a junco. It is this daytime singing, an adaptation to the High Sierra environment where cold nights preclude activity, that often attracts attention to Yosemite Toads.

In winter, they are dormant beneath the snow. As the snow melts, males, congregating in small warm-water pools, sing to attract females. Females lay short strings of eggs which develop within a week into dark tadpoles, changing shortly into toads as small as 6 mm (¼ in.) long. Under proper conditions, they may be abundant. At this young age, the males and females look alike; but as they get older, coloration and size become markedly different. Adults hide under logs and other surface objects until mating season arrives.

IDENTIFICATION
Adult males are olive-green; females and immatures have black blotches rimmed with white, brown between blotches. Parotoid glands are separated by less than the width of one gland. Usually no distinct white line down back as found in the Western Toad.

Females larger than males. Body length to 77 mm (3 in.).

Yosemite Toad Tadpole

Female Yosemite Toad
Showing Black Blotches

RANGE
Meadows of the central High Sierra. From Ebbetts Pass south to John Muir and Kaiser Passes.

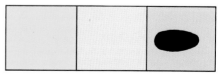

FOOTHILLS   MID-SIERRA   HIGH-SIERRA

15

Western Spadefoot

Scaphiopus hammondi

family
Pelobatidae

The Western Spadefoot is splendidly adapted to its grassland habitat which, during summer, is deadly hot and dry for most amphibians. The Spadefoot has a small black "spade" on the outer edge of each hind foot, enabling it to dig into the soil, escaping the dehydrating condition on the surface. When dormant, through summer and fall, they remain underground but after soaking rains, they make their way to temporary pools.

Males and females must find each other before their temporary pools dry up. The loud and enticing voice of the male attracts the female, his song of continuous notes somewhat like the woodpecker's hammering, and is likely to be heard on a rainy March evening. Tadpoles may change to small "adults" within a short time if the natal pool is vanishing, and may turn cannibalistic at these times.

Western Spadefoot Tadpole

"Spade" on Hind Foot

RANGE
The length of the Sierra in the grasslands of the lower foothills and Great Valley.

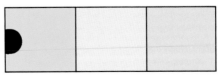

FOOTHILLS   **MID-SIERRA**   **HIGH-SIERRA**

IDENTIFICATION
The only Sierran amphibian with a *vertically elliptical pupil of the eye,* when viewed in bright light. Sole of each hind foot with a small shiny black tubercle. Often with small reddish-orange spots. Body length to 64 mm (2½ in.).

Pacific Treefrog
Hyla regilla

family
Hylidae

Few kinds of animals in the Sierra range uninterruptedly from the plains of the Great Valley to the upper lakes of the High Sierra. The Pacific Treefrog is one of the exceptions and may be found in any damp or wet environment of the Sierra, irrespective of elevation. It has even been noted by rock climbers on the cliffs of Yosemite. The adhesive toes of this treefrog make it an excellent climber.

The strong voice of this small, tailless amphibian is not restricted to the mating season and may be heard at any time of the year. Most singing occurs during the wet, cool months and at dusk or at night. A large number in a pond gives a song in unison that is quite loud, but when disturbed, they all stop suddenly. After a few minutes, the chorus usually will start again. Its voice is one of the strongest of all Sierran amphibians, and its volume is accomplished by the use of a balloon-like resonator expanded from the throat of males. The male's song is much like a loud cricket; females do not sing.

Pacific Treefrogs are preyed upon by many other animals, from Bullfrogs to garter snakes, but the widespread distribution and repro-ductive potential seem to balance the scales of nature.

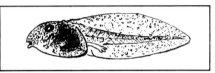

Pacific Treefrog Tadpole

IDENTIFICATION
Dark mask from tip of the nose through the eye. Small, *round adhesive discs on end of the toes.* Color varies from green through gray to brown. Wrinkled, yellowish-brown throat on males. Small - body length to 50 mm (2 in.).

RANGE
Widespread throughout the Sierra in almost any moist or wet situation. Found in all three national parks.

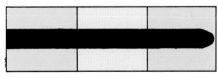

FOOTHILLS   MID-SIERRA   HIGH-SIERRA

Red-legged Frog
Rana aurora

family
Ranidae

This wary, shy amphibian doesn't announce its presence and many people will not be aware that "red legs" occur in streams they know quite well. It is the largest native frog of the Sierra and is found in permanent pools of foothill streams. When approached, it quickly and quietly seeks seclusion in the deeper part of the pool. After a while, it may come to the surface and can be seen. Hunting for it at night is often more rewarding as this amphibian favors nocturnal activity.

Breeding takes place early in the year, with the peak of egg-laying usually around the last of February. The eggs are often deposited in overflow areas near permanent pools. During the summer the tadpoles will metamorphose into frogs about 25 mm (1 in.). The voice is a low, gutteral growl, something like that of the Foothill Yellow-legged Frog. Red-legged Frogs show no special adaptation to a dry foothill environment and permanent bodies of water are necessary for survival.

The introduced Bullfrog is displacing the Red-legged Frog from its native Sierran habitat and this animal's future in the Sierra is uncertain. Suburban developments also threaten it.

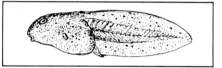

Red-Legged Frog Tadpole

IDENTIFICATION

Dark brown to light olive on back, *often with whitish "mustache."* Lower sides of belly, undersides of hind legs and feet may be reddish. Light-colored ridges (dorsolateral folds) of skin down sides of the back. Body length to 127 mm (5 in.).

RANGE

Found in only a few streams in the foothills south to the Merced River.

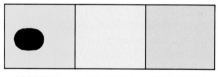

FOOTHILLS **MID-SIERRA** **HIGH-SIERRA**

Foothill Yellow-legged Frog

Rana boylei

family
Ranidae

The streams of the Sierran foothills swell dramatically in late spring and early summer with waters produced by melting snows in the High Sierra. Shortly after the peak runoff has passed, the eggs of this frog are laid in a round mass and attached to stones. The eggs develop rapidly and resulting tadpoles change into adults before the streams dry in summer. Once changed to adults, they seek out what water remains in order to survive the harsh summer, for by that time streams may well have become only a pool here and there. Under such conditions, it is common to see several of these small frogs sitting around a pool, seemingly sunbathing. When approached, they dive into the pools and hide under rocks or dig into the mud at the bottom. Some adults may even seek out springs on the hillsides, and abide there until water is again abundant.

reddish, yellowish or spotted. The underside and hind legs remain light yellow, from which the animal gets its name.

IDENTIFICATION
Color quite variable. Lower belly and inside of hind legs light yellow. Triangular patch on snout. *Usually smaller and lighter colored than the Mountain Yellow-legged Frog* and does not produce a distinctive odor when handled. Body length to 70 mm (2¾ in.).

RANGE
The length of the Sierra in foothill streams.

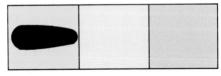

FOOTHILLS   MID-SIERRA   HIGH-SIERRA

Foothill Yellow-Legged
Frog Tadpole

This amphibian varies its color to match its background and may be

Mountain Yellow-legged Frog

Rana muscosa

family
Ranidae

A walk around a High Sierran lake will almost always reveal many frogs of this species as they jump from the bank into the water. Sometimes tadpoles are seen piled one on top of another as they lie near the edge of a lake where the water is warmer. While Yellow-legged Frogs do not resemble Bullfrogs there are several Bullfrog Lakes in the High Sierra, named after misidentified mountain frogs.

The Western Terrestrial Garter Snake preys extensively on this frog and the two animals are often found in the same area. Such close predator-prey relationship is not uncommon in fragile ecosystems. Large trout also eat tadpoles and adults.

The voice of Mountain Yellow-legged Frogs is weak and seldom heard. What role it plays is yet to be learned. Eggs are laid in warmer water during early summer and egg masses may be as large as an orange. Tadpoles usually do not metamorphose into adults until the second summer.

IDENTIFICATION

Dark brownish with blotches. *Lower belly and inside of hind leg are usually dark yellow.* When handled frequently produces a distinctive musky smell. Body length to 89 mm (3½ in.).

Unusual Black and White Variation

RANGE

A common frog in aquatic areas of the Mid and High Sierra.

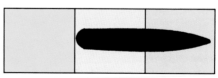

FOOTHILLS   MID-SIERRA   HIGH-SIERRA

Mountain Yellow-Legged Frog Tadpole

20

Bullfrog
Rana catesbeiana

family
Ranidae

This large, green-snouted frog is well known to all. The name Bullfrog is said to have originated from its deep, bellowing song. It is not native to the west as it was brought from the eastern United States and introduced into the Sierra in the 1920's. Now it is well established and often encountered in or near foothill ponds, streams and reservoirs, and has even displaced native frogs.

Bullfrogs often sit near the water and when disturbed, jump for the water, giving a loud squawk, before their splash. This typical behavior easily identifies Bullfrogs in the field.

The variety of the Bullfrog's diet is astounding for they seem to eat anything that moves and is small enough to swallow. They eat other frogs, including smaller Red-legged Frogs, small turtles, insects, birds, and snakes. Bullfrogs have even been known to eat small rattlesnakes.

They mate in spring and lay egg masses up to the size of a grapefruit. The tadpoles grow to be 50 mm (2 in.) in length.

IDENTIFICATION
Usually has light green snout, undersides whitish with dark spottings and no dorsolateral folds of skin. The eardrum is usually larger than the eye in males and smaller than the eye in females. The largest frog in North America. Body length to 203 mm (8 in.).

RANGE
The length of the Sierra in foothill ponds and streams. Also recorded in a few reservoirs and streams of the lower Mid-Sierra.

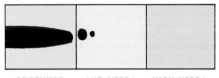

FOOTHILLS   MID-SIERRA   HIGH-SIERRA

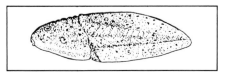

Bullfrog Tadpole

Reptiles

Reptiles form a distinct class of backboned animals, possessing a dry, cornified skin, usually with scales or scutes and lacking hair or feathers. The word reptile comes from Latin and refers to a "creeping means of locomotion."

Reptiles were the first group of vertebrate animals to adapt to life in dry environments. One expression of this adaptation is the "land egg", which enables reptiles to reproduce away from open water. This unusual egg differs markedly from the eggs of fish and amphibians by containing extra-embryonic membranes (amnion, chorion, allantois and yolk sac) that protect the developing reptile from desiccation and from physical shock; they also serve in respiration, store nitrogenous wastes, and store food.

Another adaptation of snakes and lizards to a dry environment is the production of white, semi-solid nitrogenous wastes in place of aqueous urine, as produced in mammals. Also, the cornified body covering retards the evaporation of water from the body. This dry skin further eliminates epidermal respiration, as carried on by amphibians. Reptiles breathe only by means of lungs.

All species of reptiles fertilize their eggs internally, following copulation. The Sierran reptiles that lay eggs do so in spring or early summer. The eggs are covered with a soft leathery shell, the female burying them in well aerated soil. However, some female snakes and lizards carry eggs inside of their bodies during the incubation period and give birth to living young. The developing reptiles do not obtain nourishment from the mother but only from the yolk in the eggs. The young, whether born or hatched from eggs, resemble their parents and do not go through metamorphosis, comparable to amphibians.

There are three groups of reptiles in the Sierra: turtles, lizards and snakes.

TURTLES are unparalleled in having a body encased within a protective shell composed of platelike bones covered with cornified scutes. The upper portion (carapace) and the lower portion (plastron) are connected by a "bridge" on each side. Their jaws lack teeth but have sharp, horny ridges that serve to cut and tear food. All species of turtles lay eggs following copulation and internal fertilization.

LIZARDS typically possess four easily discernable legs, each ending in five clawed toes. (The legless lizard is the only Sierran exception to this rather uniform description.) All Sierran lizards have tails with weakened zones allowing the tail to break off when seized by a predator. The tails may be regenerated in several months.

SNAKES are unequalled in their ability to swallow prey greater in diameter than themselves. This is accomplished by several peculiarities of the snake's body, which include (1) some of the skull bones are loosely joined allowing expansion of the skull, (2) the two lower jaws are joined together in front by an elastic ligament which allows them to separate, (3) the windpipe can be extended forward under the prey preventing choking during swallowing, (4) the breastbone is lacking and the free floating ribs can extend to accommodate the swallowed prey, and (5) the tissues of the esophagus, stomach and the skin easily stretch. The teeth on the jaws are sharp, needlelike, and point backward. Prey is grasped by these teeth and it is worked back into the mouth by the independent action of the jaws.

A serpent's extendible forked tongue picks up odor particles from its surroundings which are deposited on a sensitive tissue, called the Jacobson's Organ, located in the roof of the mouth. Snakes do not have external ears nor do they have movable eyelids.

Western Pond Turtle

Clemmys marmorata

family
Testudinidae

There is only one species of turtle in the Sierra and, in typical turtle fashion, it can withdraw its head, neck, legs, feet and tail within the protection of the shell. While the turtle may do this, usually it chooses not to; but instead, takes advantage of its swimming abilities to escape terrestrial enemies. This evasive maneuver is carried out easily because the turtle often basks on a rock or log near water. The turtle's excellent eyes and ears allow it to maintain a keen surveillance. This reptile is much better adapted to locomotion in water than on land; it swims quite well and can hold its breath for several minutes.

Males court females in spring. The two face each other and the male strokes the female with his long toenails; copulation follows. In late spring and early summer the female lays up to 11 eggs in a hole dug in a sand bar. The eggs hatch in about two months and the little hatchlings are about 25 mm (1 in.) long with a tail of equal length.

Frogs, insects, aquatic plants, and carrion are this turtle's food.

IDENTIFICATION
Shell olive to brown. Belly yellowish with dark spots. Length of shell to 178 mm (7 in.). Males have a more concave lower shell, longer tails and usually longer toenails than the females.

RANGE
Found the length of the Sierra in its chosen aquatic foothill haunts.

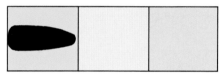

FOOTHILLS   MID-SIERRA   HIGH-SIERRA

Gilbert's Skink

Eumeces gilberti

family
Scincidae

From a tree branch, a Scrub Jay spots the bright blue tail of a young Gilbert's Skink and swoops down to attack. The jay assaults the vivid morsel with vigor, and soon finds himself busy overcoming a wriggling blue tid-bit. While the jay is struggling with the writhing tail, the now tailless skink searches out a protected spot under a rock. He, as with all Sierran lizards, has the ability to regrow his lost tail.

Skinks are seen only occasionally in the open, more commonly they are discovered under leaves, logs and rocks. In these haunts they find food consisting of small insects and other arthropods. Scorpions are part of the fare at times. Mating takes place in spring and a clutch of up to 10 eggs is laid in early summer which hatch in early fall.

IDENTIFICATION
Scales are shiny. Young have a cream and black striped body with a bright blue tail. These markings fade with age and adults are an overall shiny brown. Adult males may have orange heads, particularly in spring. Total length to 203 mm (8 in.).

Blue-Tailed Young Skink

RANGE
Found in the foothills the length of the central Sierra.

Orange Head of Adult Male
Gilbert's Skink

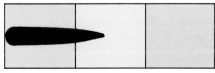

FOOTHILLS   MID-SIERRA   HIGH-SIERRA

Western Fence Lizard

Sceloporus occidentalis

family
Iguanidae

The blue markings on the underside of a male Western Fence Lizard help him establish and hold a territory and also may assist in attracting a mate. He accomplishes this by perching in a prominent location - on top of a rock or log - and displaying his vivid blue markings by repeatedly lowering his throat, raising his head, and inhaling air to increase his size. Other males are further intimidated by his curious behavior of doing "push ups." Less dominant males usually will seek an unoccupied area for their territory; occasionally they will fight for a choice spot.

Western Fence Lizard
Showing Blue Underside

This lizard is quite conspicuous as it is often seen on rocks, on logs, in trees, in wood piles and is particularly abundant on rail and rock fences. At the approach of danger they scurry under rocks, logs, or into burrows.

Females lay up to 25 soft-shelled eggs anytime between mid-May to mid-July. The eggs hatch in about two months; and these late summer or autumn hatchlings are about 25 mm (1 in.) long and lack blue markings apparent in maturity. Little growth takes place before winter dormancy, adult size being reached during the following summer. The fare of Western Fence Lizards consists of beetles, flies, wasps, termites, ants, and spiders. The Sierra Fence Lizard (*Sceloporus occidentalis taylori*), a subspecies inhabiting High Sierra canyons, has a solid blue belly and throat, and may even be blue on top. Western Fence Lizards in the rest of the Sierra lack the blue marking down the middle of the belly.

IDENTIFICATION
Black or blotched brownish-gray on top. *Throat and belly blue,* less pronounced in females and young. Distinctly pointed keeled scales on top. Scales on back of thigh mostly keeled. Total length to 204 mm (8 in.).

RANGE
The length of the Sierra, primarily in the foothills.

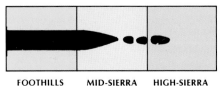

FOOTHILLS   **MID-SIERRA**   **HIGH-SIERRA**

26

Sagebrush Lizard

Sceloporus graciosus

family
Iguanidae

Quiet little lizards such as this type easily may go unobserved, but once one learns to recognize them and knows their habits, they add to the enjoyment of the mountains. Watch for them under dense bushes, in downed branches and on rocks and logs. The Sagebrush Lizard resembles its close relative, the Western Fence Lizard, and adult males of each species have blue bellies. Neither lizard is poisonous. Coloration is important to the survival of each species by the role it plays in the establishment of territories. Each lizard does "push ups" to help display its blue undersides; this behavior also serves them as a means of recognition of individuals. They increase the rate of "push ups" when enemies approach. This also assists them in gaining a three dimensional perspective of their surroundings.

Mating occurs in spring and in early summer, with up to seven soft-shelled eggs laid in damp soil; these hatch in the fall. The orange color on the sides of some females may indicate that mating has taken place and the lizard is near the time of egg-laying. Their diet consists of a variety of small moving insects.

IDENTIFICATION

Distinctly blotched and brownish on top. Throat and belly light blue, less pronounced or missing in females and young. Orange on sides of some adult females. Has relatively smaller scales than Western Fence Lizard and has granular (not keeled) scales on back of thigh. Total length to 128 mm (5 in.).

RANGE

The length of the Sierra at middle elevations.

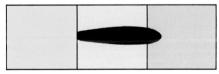

FOOTHILLS   MID-SIERRA   HIGH-SIERRA

27

Western Whiptail

Cnemidophorus tigris

family
Teiidae

Sprinting characterizes this fast-running lizard and its speed provides a major protection from enemies. Its hind legs are large and strong, with long, slender toes on the feet; the combination accounts for its speed. The tail, too, is long and slender, accounting for its common name - whiptail. When walking, the lizard drags its tail, leaving an easily identifiable track.

When foraging, it moves in a distinct jerking manner which produces a characteristic sound - particularly in dry leaves. If disturbed while hunting in the open, it will run to the nearest protective cover with a burst of speed, usually choosing a bush. If it finds this cover inadequate, it will run from bush to bush until adequate cover is found. When further startled, it may be heard scurrying through the dense underbrush.

Usually a hole or crevice is "home" for the Western Whiptail. If the ground is soft enough, the lizard will dig its own burrow.

Fare for whiptails is insects and spiders, but has been known to be cannibalistic and also to eat the eggs of other lizards.

Mating occurs in May and June, up to 10 eggs are laid in June and July, to hatch in the fall. Its habitat is hot, dry open areas such as along the sides of paved roads or on unpaved roads and trails.

IDENTIFICATION
Tiger-like coloration, long tail and pointed snout. Bead-like scales. Hind legs larger than fore legs. Total length to 355 mm (14 in.).

RANGE
The length of the Sierra in the lower foothills.

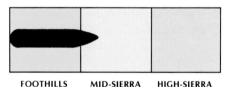

FOOTHILLS   MID-SIERRA   HIGH-SIERRA

Southern Alligator Lizard

Gerrhonotus multicarinatus

**family
Anguidae**

When approached by an enemy, this lizard will sometimes turn toward the intruder and, with mouth agape, stand his ground. This strategy sometimes works and while the attacker is "thinking things over," the lizard seeks shelter and safety. The large head and long body gives rise to the common name "alligator lizard." If handled, it can give a real nip with its powerful jaws.

Lizards as a group, seldom hang by their tails, as their tails readily break off, but, the Southern Alligator Lizard does just that and in addition uses the tail almost as a fifth hand.

It has a varied diet: spiders, including Black Widows, insects, snails, bird eggs and fledglings, and small mammals. It has even been known to dive into pools to catch tadpoles.

Mating occurs in April to June and up to 20 eggs are laid in burrows or under rocks in July and August, hatching in the fall.

IDENTIFICATION
May be a large lizard, total length to 305 mm (12 in.) with proportionately large head. Long body with a fold of skin along its sides, legs relatively small, tail may be long. Color varies from green to reddish. Dark *longitudinal stripes on belly down the middle of the scale rows.* Males are often larger and have a more distinctly triangular head than females.

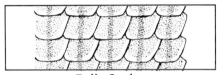
Belly Scales

RANGE
The length of the Sierra in brushy and rocky areas of the foothills.

FOOTHILLS   MID-SIERRA   HIGH-SIERRA

29

Northern Alligator Lizard

Gerrhonotus coeruleus

family
Anguidae

The Mid-Sierra and High Sierra are inhabited by this reptile. It possesses specific adaptations which enable it to live at these high elevations. For one thing, it functions at a lower body temperature (20° to 30° C) than lizards of warmer areas; and for another, the eggs are retained inside the female until the young are born. An expectant mother acts as a living incubator, moving from one warm, sunny spot to another, in order to absorb sufficient heat to warm her body, and thus incubate the eggs.

Mating occurs in May and June, and up to 10 young are born in the fall. At birth, the young are about 50 mm (2 in.) long and must fend for themselves, as there is no parental care.

This lizard eats insects, spiders and millipedes. It is occasionally seen away from protective cover, but more often it is found near or under bushes, bark, and rocks. Some hikers have been surprised to see this reptile take to the water to escape them. It swims quite well.

Alligator lizards do not move as fast as most lizards and can be overtaken and captured by hand. When caught, they will turn and bite. The bite is not painful.

IDENTIFICATION

Coloration varies from dark gray to a blotched green. Dark longi-tudinal *stripes on belly between the scale rows.* Dorsal scales in 16 rows. Fold of skin down its sides. Dark eyes. Total length to 205 mm (8 in.).

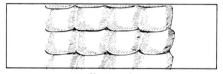

Belly Scales

RANGE

The length of the Sierra at middle and high elevations.

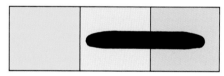

FOOTHILLS   MID-SIERRA   HIGH-SIERRA

California
Legless Lizard
Anniella pulchra

family
Anniellidae

The absence of legs does not always distinguish snakes from lizards, and the California Legless Lizard demonstrates this point. The lizard characteristic of movable eyelids, small scales on the underside and firm anterior attachment of the lower jaw bones are in evidence. The legless lizard is well-adapted to its burrowing life. It has no ear openings to become clogged with dirt, its nostrils can be closed, its counter-sunk lower jaw shuts firmly and its smooth skin offers little friction. Legs are a disadvantage to some burrowers and they have been lost during the evolution of this lizard. The dark, underground environment has placed a premium on the sense of touch and smell instead of sight, and these are well developed.

Its food consists mainly of insects, such as beetle larvae, encountered while burrowing. The female retains the eggs; one to four young are born in the fall of the year.

IDENTIFICATION
Snakelike but no forked tongue and no transverse plates on ventral surface. *Silvery to beige above and yellow below* with small black line down the middle of the back. Rounded head and tail. Total length to 180 mm (7 in.).

RANGE
Its Sierra distribution is restricted to the foothills of the Kaweah River drainage where it burrows in sandy soil or decaying leaves. Streamside Bush Lupine is often an indicator of appropriate legless lizard habitat.

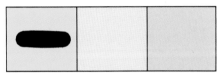

FOOTHILLS   MID-SIERRA   HIGH-SIERRA

31

Rubber Boa

Charina bottae

family
Boidae

This docile animal is the only Sierran member of the ancient boa family, the male having the characteristic remnants of hind legs in the form of anal spurs. This lizardlike characteristic has not been lost as is the case with most other snake families. Its skull bones are more solidly fused than in most snakes; this aids in burrowing, which the Rubber Boa does well. When above ground, it is subject to attack by a variety of predators. When attacked, it may hide its head under the coils of its body and exposes its blunt tail as a decoy for its head. Scarred tails verify the effectiveness of this behavior.

Defensive Pose

Though the pupils of its small eyes are vertically elliptical, like those of some poisonous snakes, the snake is completely harmless. It is a slow-moving, non-aggressive animal that is often mistreated, like most serpents, but never bites in retaliation.

Its diet consists of small rodents, lizards and fledgling birds. The rodents and birds are squeezed until they stop moving and then are swallowed. Lizards are swallowed without constriction, as they are taken in the cooler hours, when they generally are immobile.

These snakes do not lay eggs, but retain the eggs and up to six young are born in the early fall.

IDENTIFICATION
A *plain brown snake with shiny, smooth skin.* Yellowish underside. Small head and blunt, head-like tail. Total length to 736 mm (29 in.).

RANGE
Rubber Boas occur the entire length of the Sierra. They are usually encountered along Mid-Sierran streams, around meadows, and occasionally on the forest floor. They are primarily active in the early morning and at dusk.

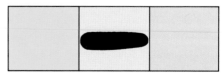

FOOTHILLS   MID-SIERRA   HIGH-SIERRA

Ringneck Snake

Diadophis punctatus

family
Colubridae

A small, docile serpent such as the Ringneck Snake is subject to attack by a variety of predators and thus it needs protection, but it is neither poisonous nor fast. When disturbed, the ringneck often turns on its back or coils its tail and turns the downside up, exposing the red underside to an attacker. This red coloration serves to startle attackers; the snake then quickly seeks cover to survive a while longer. Ringnecks are favorite snakes to many because of their bright color, interesting behavior and gentleness. As with other snakes, secretive habits prevent its being observed often.

Food consists of slender salamanders, Pacific Treefrogs, small lizards, earthworms, and perhaps insects. There is growing evidence that this snake eats the tails from slender salamanders and allows the body to escape and regrow its tail.

Up to six eggs are laid in early summer, hatching in early fall.

IDENTIFICATION
Topside is olive, bluish or nearly *black with red-orange neck band.* Underside is red-orange with black dots; the underside of the tail often being the most brightly colored portion. Small snake, total length usually under 457 mm (18 in.).

RANGE
The length of the Sierra, found beneath logs, rocks and loose leaves in damp places in the foothills.

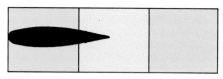

FOOTHILLS   MID-SIERRA   HIGH-SIERRA

Sharp-tailed Snake

Contia tenuis

family
Colubridae

The function of the sharp spine on the end of this small snake's tail is not fully understood. It may be used as an anchor when the reptile struggles with slugs, the serpent's primary food. Adaptive modification of the tail is not restricted to this species of snake, but is also noted with the Rubber Boa, Ring-neck Snake, and Western Rattle-snake. The loss of limbs in the evolution of snakes has apparently placed a greater survival value on the tail and its functions. Lizards, which have retained their legs, do not show such a degree of variation in the use of their tails.

The Sharp-tailed Snake mates in spring; in summer it lays up to 8 eggs which hatch in the fall.

Steller's Jays and other birds attack sharp-tails, but surface objects such as logs, bark, twigs, and rocks provide these small snakes hiding places from such enemies. Most snakes spend much of their lives in seclusion to avoid contact with predators. Snakes, particularly sharp-tails, may occur in larger numbers than casual observations indicate.

IDENTIFICATION
Small, shiny, reddish-brown or gray snake. Tail with sharp point. Whitish line down side with alter-nating black and cream bars across belly. Smooth scales. Total length to 350 mm (14 in.).

RANGE
The length of the Sierra in the foothills and lower Mid-Sierra.

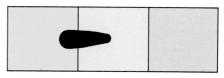

FOOTHILLS   MID-SIERRA   HIGH-SIERRA

34

Racer

Coluber constrictor

family
Colubridae

The common name Racer is deserved by this speedy serpent. Comparative studies indicate that this species may be the fastest of all snakes, moving as fast as a person can run. It is also a curious animal and will advance, head up, toward objects it has sensed but not recognized; however, upon recognizing humans it retires quickly. When cornered or captured, it is often aggressive and bites. It is uncommon in the central Sierra but becomes more common in the northern Sierra. Its food consists of small rodents, birds, other reptiles, amphibians, and insects. Prey is not killed by

Breeding occurs in spring and up to 25 eggs are laid in early summer, hatching in late summer or early fall. At hatching, the young are up to 305 mm (12 in.) in length but are not colored like the parents. Rather, they look much like small Gopher Snakes, but are unlike them in having large eyes and shiny unkeeled scales. Young snakes are more often encountered than adults.

IDENTIFICATION
Above, a uniform blue gray to olive green to tan. Belly yellow. Slender body with large eyes. Total length to 1270 mm (50 in.).

RANGE
Primarily found in foothill grasslands, but has been recorded from brushlands, meadows, and grassy river borders. Found the length of the Sierra.

Young Racer

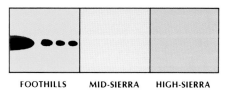

FOOTHILLS   MID-SIERRA   HIGH-SIERRA

constriction, but is grabbed by sharp, recurved teeth and swallowed.

Striped Racer

Masticophus lateralis

family
Colubridae

Speed characterizes this alert serpent as it does its unstriped relative of the grasslands, the Racer. In addition to being fast on the ground, the Striped Racer is also a good climber and moves quickly through bushes. This quickness provides the snakes a defense from pursuer as well as being useful in capturing prey.

Its diet is varied, consisting of small mammals, bird eggs and young birds, amphibians, lizards, and other snakes - including rattlesnakes. The prey is not constricted, but is grabbed with the mouth and held by the snake's sharp teeth while being swallowed.

Snakes have two penises housed in the base of the tail which are unsheathed at the time of copulation. Copulation with most snakes takes place on the ground; but in the case of the Striped Racer, it also takes place in bushes. Mating occurs in spring and up to eight eggs are laid in early summer which hatch in late summer or early fall.

IDENTIFICATION

Black to dark brown back with a *pale yellow to cream colored stripe along each side of the back.* Smooth scales and large eyes. Slender and fast. May move with its head held up above the ground. Total length to 1523 mm (60 in.).

RANGE

This snake is closely associated with the upper foothill brushlands, rocky areas, and along streams the entire length of the Sierra.

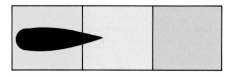

FOOTHILLS   MID-SIERRA   HIGH-SIERRA

Common Kingsnake

Lampropeltis getulus

family
Colubridae

This docile snake rarely bites and then only when first handled. When disturbed, it vibrates its tail and, if in dry leaves, makes an alarming sound, similar to a rattlesnake. Kingsnakes are famous for eating other snakes, particularly rattlesnakes, which probably accounts for the feeling that they are king of snakes. Often rattlesnakes can smell the presence of a kingsnake and quickly will leave the area, head held close to the ground. Kingsnakes are relatively immune to the venom of rattlesnakes. Small mammals, frogs, lizards, salamanders and birds are also eaten. Sometimes, they will hunt birds' nests on or near the ground, eating the eggs, fledglings, or adults.

Mating occurs in spring and early summer and up to 12 eggs are laid in moist soil two months later. Twelve-inch-long young come from the eggs in about another two months. This reptile occupies a variety of habitats and is found in the open as well as under surface objects.

Common Kingsnake
Notice Smooth Shiny Scales

RANGE
The length of the Sierra foothills.

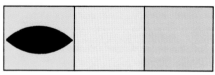

FOOTHILLS   MID-SIERRA   HIGH-SIERRA

IDENTIFICATION
Conspicuous coloration of *alternating black (sometimes brown) and white bands.* Smooth shiny scales. Total length to 1523 mm (60 in.).

California Mountain Kingsnake

Lampropeltis zonata

family
Colubridae

What a pleasant thrill to come upon one of these colorful animals. Unfortunately, the distinctive coloration of this harmless kingsnake sometimes results in it being mis-identified as a poisonous coral snake and unjustly killed. Coral snakes do not occur in the Sierra. The pattern of rings in combination with color cause predators to avoid this reptile.

Snakes have a keen sense of smell and are stimulated by odors during courtship and mating. As with all snakes, this species produces its own characteristic odor which is quite pronounced when the snake is first handled. The function of these odors is not fully understood.

Its food consists of lizards, eggs (birds and lizards), nestling birds and other small snakes. When necessary, the prey is killed by constriction, otherwise the prey is grabbed with the mouth and swallowed. Mating takes place in late spring; up to six eggs are laid in early summer, to hatch in fall.

IDENTIFICATION

Colorful shiny snake with *black, red and white bands*. Rarely the red bands are incomplete or missing, particularly on smaller snakes. Black snout. Total length to 1049 mm (41 in.).

RANGE

Moist, cool canyons are favored by California Mountain Kingsnakes but they are also encountered in forested areas. Found the length of the Sierra up to 2409 meters (8,100 ft).

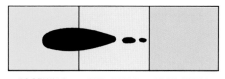

FOOTHILLS   MID-SIERRA   HIGH-SIERRA

Common Garter Snake

Thamnophis sirtalis

family

Colubridae

The garter snakes (genus *Thamnophis*) are familiar to nearly all who leave the city since they frequent ponds, streams, lakes, and meadows which are also the haunts of hikers, picnickers, and fishermen.

When grabbed by a person or predator these harmless fellows sometimes bite, though not hard, and often smear a foul smelling anal fluid on themselves and their captor. This behavior is somewhat effective in discouraging predators and particularly effective with humans.

When cornered, the Common Garter Snake will inflate its body and exhibit red markings along its sides intended to alarm and drive off predators.

Small rodents, birds, lizards, frogs, tadpoles, salamanders and fish are part of its varied diet; one was recorded swimming in a pool with a six-inch Rainbow Trout in its mouth.

Mating occurs in spring, apparently aided by odors produced by both the male and female snakes. The eggs are retained within the female, and up to 50 four-inch-long young are born alive in summer.

IDENTIFICATION

Black, gray or dark brown with a distinct cream colored stripe down the middle of the back. *Sides usually blotched with red.* Usually 7 upper labial scales. Keeled scales. Length to 1270 mm (50 in.).

RANGE

Foothill streams the length of the Sierra.

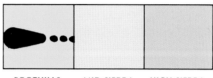

FOOTHILLS   MID-SIERRA   HIGH-SIERRA

Western Aquatic Garter Snake

Thamnophis couchi

family
Colubridae

The Western Aquatic Garter Snake is a common resident of foothill aquatic sites and often is seen by fishermen, as it basks in the sun on rocks or in warm water at a stream's edge. It is an excellent swimmer and when disturbed, it dives deep into a pool, hiding there under submerged rocks. After a few minutes, it may be seen coming up for a breath of air.

Fishermen sometimes condemn garter snakes for they too catch fish. Tadpoles, frogs, and salamanders are also eaten, though this is not lamented by fishermen.

Mating takes place during the spring, the eggs retained within the mother, with up to 30 five-inch-long young being born in late summer.

IDENTIFICATION
Back is a blotched brown to black. May have a faint stripe on head and short distance down back. No red sides. Keeled scales, usually 8 upper labial scales. Total length to 1270 mm (50 in.).

RANGE
Upper foothill streams the length of the Sierra.

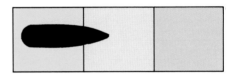

FOOTHILLS   MID-SIERRA   HIGH-SIERRA

40

Western Terrestrial Garter Snake

Thamnophis elegans

**family
Colubridae**

The common name of this snake is misleading as it is encountered usually in the High and Mid-Sierra in lakes, streams and in meadows. It swims well and often enters the water to escape enemies. Mountain Yellow-legged Frogs inhabit these same areas and the Western Terrestrial Garter Snake preys extensively upon the adults and tadpoles of this amphibian. It also eats trout, Pacific Treefrogs and small rodents. It is the most common reptile of the High Sierra and is known to most backpackers.

Mating takes place in early summer; the retention of eggs by the mother is a feature of this species that enables survival in the cold High Sierra. Young are born in summer to fall, depending on elevation.

IDENTIFICATION

Distinct whitish mid-dorsal stripe bordered by black or dark brown with another light colored dorso-lateral stripe. Usually 8 upper labial scales. Keeled scales. Total length to 1070 mm (42 in.).

RANGE

In the Mid and High Sierra along the length of the range.

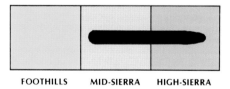

FOOTHILLS   MID-SIERRA   HIGH-SIERRA

Night Snake

Hypsiglena torquata

family
Colubridae

This gentle snake is poisonous, producing small quantities of venom that are injected into lizards and other small animals by grooved teeth located in the rear of the mouth. The venom serves to subdue the prey. Larger animals, including humans, are not threatened by this serpent's poisonous bite.

As its name implies, this creature is nocturnal and should be watched for while driving along foothill roads at night.

Mating takes place in early spring, and up to 8 eggs are laid in late spring, to hatch in late summer.

IDENTIFICATION

Overall light brown with dark blotches, *larger dark brown blotches on each side of neck.* Eye with vertical pupil. Smooth scales. Length to 510 mm (20 in.).

RANGE

This snake has been encountered from the western edge of the foothills up into the lower Mid-Sierra. It appears to have a spotty distribution the length of the Sierra. Local populations of snakes are occasionally encountered during road construction, mining, and other forms of excavating.

FOOTHILLS   MID-SIERRA   HIGH-SIERRA

Gopher Snake
Pituophis melanoleucus

family
Colubridae

The vicious, aggressive attitude often taken by a Gopher Snake is merely a bluff to startle or frighten away an intruder, after which the snake makes haste for a safer spot. Gopher Snake coloration and behavior are much like a rattlesnake's and the resemblance probably provides a degree of protection from predators. Sometimes in dry grass or leaves, its vibrating tail will produce a buzzing sound which, when combined with seeing the snake, brings about misidentification - rattlesnake!

Small animals such as gophers, mice, ground squirrels and small rabbits make up most of this serpent's fare, and often the snake inhabits the same burrows as its prey. The snake squeezes its prey until movements stop, then it is swallowed whole.

Mating occurs in spring and up to 12 eggs are laid in early summer; these hatch in late summer or early fall. The young are about 153 mm (6 in.) long at hatching.

IDENTIFICATION
Yellow or buff with black, brown or reddish brown blotches on back. Keeled scales. Pointed tail. Total length to 2134 mm (7 ft.).

RANGE
This common diurnal snake is found in many different habitats the length of the Sierra.

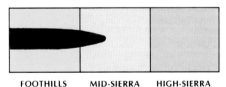

FOOTHILLS MID-SIERRA HIGH-SIERRA

Gopher Snake,
Buff with Brown Variation

43

Western Black-headed Snake

Tantilla planiceps

family
Colubridae

Even dedicated students of Sierra reptiles seldom come across this secretive snake. The snake was first collected in the Sierra in the 1930's. The author was quite excited when he found one, eight kilometers (5 mi.) northeast of Orosi, Tulare County in 1963. During the summer of 1975, a dead specimen was picked up at Ash Mountain in Sequoia National Park. It had a beetle larva lodged in its mouth and had apparently died during its swallowing efforts. The snake's small size and retiring habits make it hard to find, but it is felt that more will be discovered as interest in this animal increases.

The Black-headed Snake spends most of its life underground in crevices and burrows, but may be discovered under logs, rocks and boards.

Outside the Sierra, females are reported to lay up to four eggs in spring which hatch in 60 to 90 days. Eggs and young snakes have not been found and studied in the Sierra.

Spiders, soft-bodied insects, centipedes and earthworms are the likely food of this serpent. Little detailed information about the food of this serpent is available from the Sierra.

IDENTIFICATION
Black head. Body is a shiny brown to gray above with a reddish stripe down the belly. Usually small, up to 380 mm (15 in.) in total length.

RANGE
Reported only from the foothills of Tulare County.

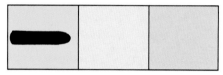

FOOTHILLS	MID-SIERRA	HIGH-SIERRA

44

Western Rattlesnake
Crotalus viridis

family
Viperidae

When new-born, the end of a rattlesnake's tail has a blunt rounded segment, the prebutton, which is soundless. Usually within a week, the outer cornified layer of the snake's skin is shed and the prebutton is replaced by a bell-shaped segment, the button. Thereafter, each time this portion of the skin is shed, a new loose-fitting segment is added to the now audible rattle. Environmental temperature, availability of food, age, and sex are some of the factors that effect the frequency of skin-shedding. Also, the rattle is made of a brittle material, much like fingernails, resulting in the rattle segments wearing and breaking off easily; therefore, the age of a rattlesnake may not always be determined by counting the number of segments in a rattle.

The rattle does not produce a rattling sound, as the name implies, but rather a buzzing sound, 45 to 55 hertz. This type sound is known to frighten a variety of animals, which evidently associate the buzzing with danger. Rattlesnakes rattle when they want to be left alone and the buzzing sound should be considered as a warning. The rattle is silent when the snake is hunting, as the sound would frighten away potential meals, nor does the snake always rattle before striking enemies.

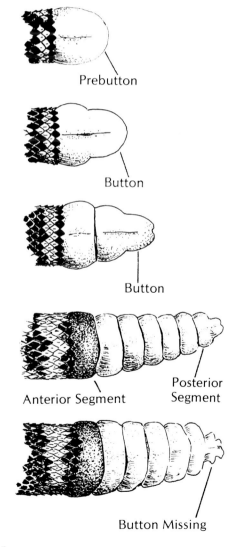

Prebutton

Button

Button

Anterior Segment

Posterior Segment

Button Missing

Many animals are not seriously intimidated by a rattlesnake or its sound effects. Black Bears, Common Ravens and Red-tailed Hawks, as well as other animals, are known to prey on rattlesnakes. Common Kingsnakes, like other snakes, can not hear air borne sounds, thus prey on rattlesnakes.

Rattlesnake venom, a complex fluid containing toxins and enzymes, is produced in two modified salivary glands lying on each side of the snake's head behind the eyes. A snake is thought to have control over the amount of venom injected during a bite and an animal may be bitten and no venom injected, depending upon the snake's behavior. Venom is injected by the squeezing of muscles over the poison producing glands which forces the venom through ducts and on through two hollow, needle-like fangs. Most of the time the fangs are folded up into the top of the mouth to be extended as the snake opens its mouth during the strike. When a prey animal is struck, it usually jumps and may break off one or both of the serpent's fangs. The snake then employs reserve fangs, folded deep in the roof of its mouth. A new fang may move down into the functional position within a few hours.

The snake's venom is used primarily and very effectively to obtain food. By the use of poison, the rattlesnake is able to kill animals that otherwise might be too large to subdue. When the rattlesnake is young, it eats lizards and mice, turning to larger prey as it grows. California Ground Squirrels are a primary food of adult rattlesnakes in the foothills; but other rodents, small rabbits and some birds also are eaten. Golden-mantled Ground Squirrels, chipmunks, and Deer Mice make up most of the diet at higher elevations.

Rattlesnakes see quite well in either bright or dim light. About five days before shedding the outer layer of their skin, the eyes become temporarily clouded with a milky colored fluid. This prepares the clear scale over the eye so it too may be shed. The snake is blind for about a day, after which the eye clears and sight is restored. The detection of warm-bodied animals, birds and mammals, is aided further by temperature-sensitive organs located on each side of a rattlesnake's face. These facial pits, (which give rise to the name pit-viper), allow the snake to detect even slight temperature changes in its surroundings. By moving its head back-and-forth, a snake is able to "zero-in" on a warm-bodied animal, even in total darkness.

A rattlesnake strikes, injects venom then withdraws from the victim, all in an instant. The prey does not die immediately, but instead, runs varying distances before being disabled by the poison. The rattlesnake then tracks down the meal by the use of its keen sense of smell, which is aided by a delicate forked tongue. The moist tongue, which is extended without opening the mouth, picks up odor particles, which are placed by the retracted tongue on sensitive tissue, called Jacobson's Organ, located in the roof of the mouth.

Rattlesnake Strike

Anticipating dormancy, some rattlesnakes move in late fall to a den usually located in a cave or deep rocky crevice where they spend the winter. These dens occur more often in the Mid-Sierra and higher foothills than at lower elevations. One den encountered by the author on 13 November 1963 was at 1,067 metres (3,500 ft.) elevation and contained 54 snakes of varying sizes.

Rattlesnakes usually come out of winter dormancy when the environmental temperature reaches 21°C (70°F) which usually occurs in March in the foothills. Hot, direct sunlight will overheat and kill a rattlesnake within 15 minutes. The snake maintains its optimum body temperature by moving back and forth between shade and sun or during hot months, at lower elevations, it may be active at dawn, dusk or at night.

Within a few weeks after emergence from the winter den, the annual mating takes place. Fertilization of eggs is internal, following copulation. The eggs are retained within the female and up to fourteen young, measuring to 350 mm (12 in.) in length are born in the fall. If it has been an early, warm spring, mating will be earlier and the young born in late September; if spring has been cold, the young are born later. The young usually shed the outer layer of their skin once before entering winter dormancy.

Rattlesnakes can swim quite well, the long right lung, charac-

"Milk" Eye before Shedding

teristic of most snakes, providing increased bouyancy. They usually hold their rattles high and dry and may strike while in water.

Rattlesnake bites have caused human death; but they are not a serious threat because they are seldom encountered, particularly

Rattlesnake Showing Pits and Forked Tongue

in the High Sierra. It is still wise to gain knowledge of their habits and treat them with the respect they deserve. Almost all rattlesnake bites can be prevented, as rattlesnakes usually are touched before they bite a human. Bites can be avoided by watching carefully where one walks, puts one's hands or sits. Don't pick up any snake which has not been correctly identified and don't ever pick up a rattlesnake. Avoid cutting the rattle off a not-quite-dead snake, as a severed head has a temporary capacity to bite. Occasionally, people set on killing a rattlesnake have been bitten when picking up a stick or other weapon lying within striking distance of a coiled snake. A wise person keeps a safe distance from rattlesnakes at all times.

The treatment of rattlesnake bite is a popular topic but ideas about treatment are changing and the reader is asked to consult the American Red Cross for the latest accepted methods on the subject.

Western Rattlesnake

IDENTIFICATION
Varies in color from cream to black with blotches. Stout bodied, tapering tail with a series of inter-locking pieces of dry skin called a rattle. *Head is broad, flat, triangular,* and has vertically elliptical pupils in the eyes when in bright light. Facial pits present. Scales are distinctly keeled. Total length to 680 mm (5½ ft.).

RANGE
The length of the Sierra, mostly in the foothills but recorded up to 3,355 meters (11,000 ft.).

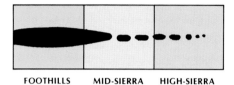

FOOTHILLS   MID-SIERRA   HIGH-SIERRA

48

Index

A

Ambystoma macrodactylum, 5
Ambystoma tigrinum, 4
Amphibians (text), 1, 3
Aneides lugubris, 9
Anniella pulchra, 31
Arboreal Salamander, 9

B

Bathachoseps attenuatus, 13
Bathachoseps relictus, 12
Bufo boreas, 14
Bufo canorus, 15
Bullfrog, 21

C

California Legless Lizard, 31
California Mountain Kingsnake, 38
California Newt, 6
California Slender Salamander, 13
Charina bottae, 32
Clemmys marmorata, 24
Cnemidophorus tigris, 28
Coluber constrictor, 35
Common Garter Snake, 39
Common Kingsnake, 37
Contia tenuis, 34
Crotalus viridis, 45

D

Diadophis punctatus, 33

E

Ensatina, 7
Ensatina eschscholtzi, 7
Eumeces gilberti, 25

F

Foothill Yellow-Legged Frog, 19
FROGS,
  Bullfrog, 21
  Foothil Yellow-Legged, 19
  Mountain Yellow-Legged, 20
  Pacific Treefrog, 17
  Red-Legged, 18

G

Gerhonotus coeruleus, 30
Gerrhonotus multicarinatus, 29
Gilbert's Skink, 25
Gopher Snake, 43

H

Hydromantes brunus, 11
Hydromantes platycephalus, 10
Hyla regilla, 17
Hypsiglena torquata, 42

L

Lampropeltis getulus, 37
Lampropeltis zonata, 38
Limestone Salamander, 11
LIZARDS,
  California Legless, 31
  Gilbert's Skink, 25
  Northern Alligator, 30
  Sagebrush, 27
  Southern Alligator, 29
  Western Fence, 26
  Western Whiptail, 28
Long-Toed Salamander, 5

M

Masticophis lateralis, 36
Mount Lyell Salamander, 10
Mountain Yellow-Legged Frog, 20

N

Night Snake, 42
Northern Alligator Lizard, 30

P

Pacific Treefrog, 17
Pituophis melanoleucus, 43

R

Racer, 35
Rana aurora, 18
Rana boylei, 19
Rana catesbeiana, 21
Rana muscosa, 20
Red-legged Frog, 18
Relictual Slender Salamander, 12
Reptiles (text), 22, 23
Ringneck Snake, 33
Rubber Boa, 32

S

Sagebrush lizard, 27
SALAMANDERS,
  Arboreal, 9
  California Newt, 6
  California Slender, 13

Ensatina, 7
Limestone, 11
Long-Toed, 5
Mount Lyell, 10
Relictual Slender, 12
Tiger, 4
Scaphiopus hammondi, 16
Sceloporus graciosus, 27
Sceloporus occidentalis, 26
Sharp-Tailed Snake, 34
SNAKES,
    California Mountain King, 38
    Common Garter, 39
    Common King, 37
    Gopher, 43
    Night, 42
    Racer, 35
    Ringneck, 33
    Rubber Boa, 32
    Sharp-Tailed, 34
    Striped Racer, 36
    Western Black-Headed, 44
    Western Aquatic Garter, 40
    Western Terrestrial Garter, 41
    Western Rattlesnake, 45
Southern Alligator Lizard, 29
    Striped Racer, 36

T
Tantilla planiceps, 44
Thamnophis couchi, 40
Thamnophis elegans, 41
Thamnophis sirtalis, 39
Tiger Salamander, 4
Taricha torosa, 6
TURTLE,
    Western Pond, 24
TOADS,
    Western, 14
    Yosemite, 15
W
Western Aquatic Garter Snake, 40
Western Black-Headed Snake, 44
Western Fence Lizard, 26
    Western Pond Turtle, 24
    Western Rattlesnake, 45
    Western Spadefoot, 16
    Western Terrestrial Garter Snake, 41
    Western Toad, 14
Western Whiptail, 28
Y
Yosemite Toad, 15